THE
SILENT FIELD

36 aires and country dances
arranged for solo guitar
by
Michael Raven

Dedicated to the
memory of my mother,
Marion Raven (1909–1992)

Foreword

The pieces in this series of books have been printed in approximate performance order. However, the player should feel absolutey free to re-arrange them into aire-dance pairs, or suites of three or more tunes, as his fancy takes him. He should also feel free to alter and adapt, to make the music his own.

There are many strong melodies here and these provide excellent material for those interested in making extended works. In this respect one has to do little more than add arpeggio, tremolo and rasgueado sections, throw in a few harmonics and a bit of pizzicato bass, and one has a concert solo of grand design. Seriously, though, we are now in the new age of the composer-performer and there can be little doubt that such past masters as John Dowland and Fernando Sor are looking down and applauding; they are flattered by the endless performances of their undoubtedly excellent compositions, flattered but mightily bored.

Michael Raven,

Published by: Michael Raven
                 Yew Tree Cottage
                 Jug Bank, Ashley
                 Market Drayton
                 Shropshire TF9 4NJ
                 Tel: 0630 672304

First Edition: March 1993

Copyright: All arrangements
                 Michael Raven. The
                 following are original
                 compositions by
                 Michael Raven:
                 Guajira (part of)
                 Mandrake
                 Cradle Song
                 Cows in the Corn
                 Mexican Serenade
                 Woodpecker's Jig
                 Mills of Strata Marcella
                 My Last Farewell
                 Red Velvet
                 Silent Field
                 Swynnerton Blackbird
                 Epitaph
                 Fair Land
                 Foaming Jug
                 Copyright Michael Raven 1993 ©
                 All rights reserved.

Front cover:
Winter scene at Derrington,
near Stafford.
Photograph by M.Raven,
circa 1991.

Contents

Guajira

Guajira is a Mexican indian word meaning 'lady'. It is the name of a popular Cuban song type characterized by alternating bars of 6/8 and 3/4 which has been adopted by flamenco musicians. It is played at a slow to moderate tempo and should have a lyrical quality. As in most flamenco forms (or toques) a basic riff alternates with a succession of short tunes, some traditional and some composed by the performer. Of the music printed here the basic riff and tunes 1 and 2 are traditional; tunes 3, 4 and 5 and the concluding rasgueado were written by Michael Raven.

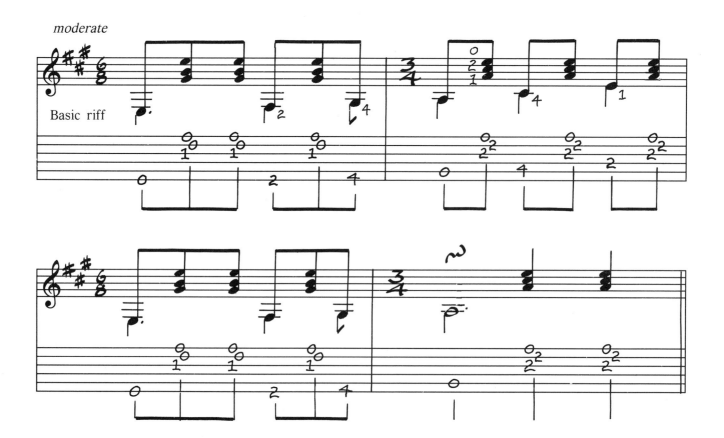

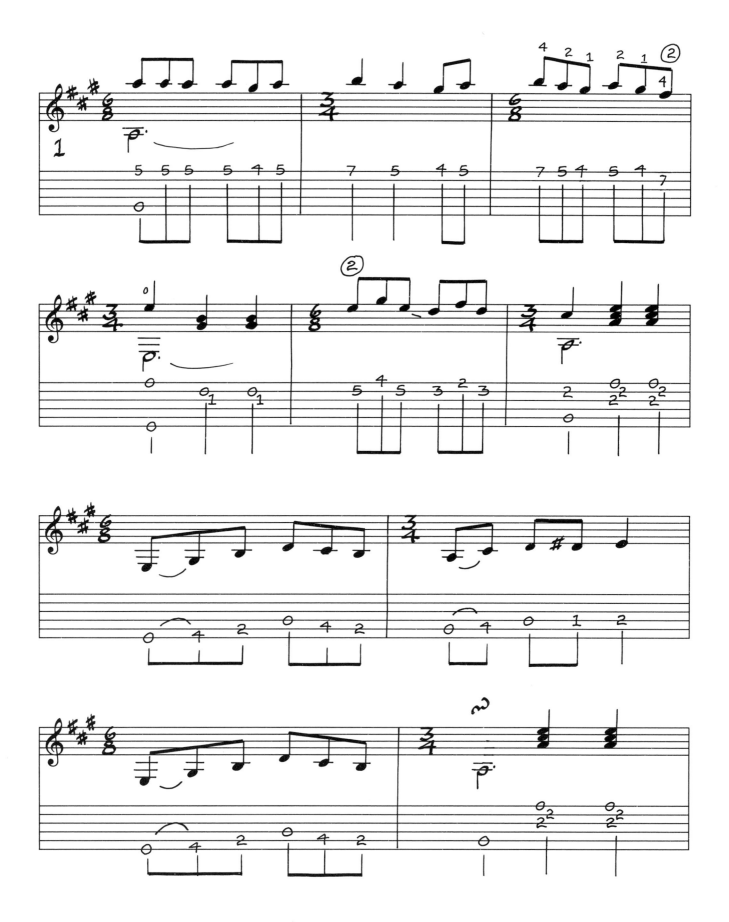

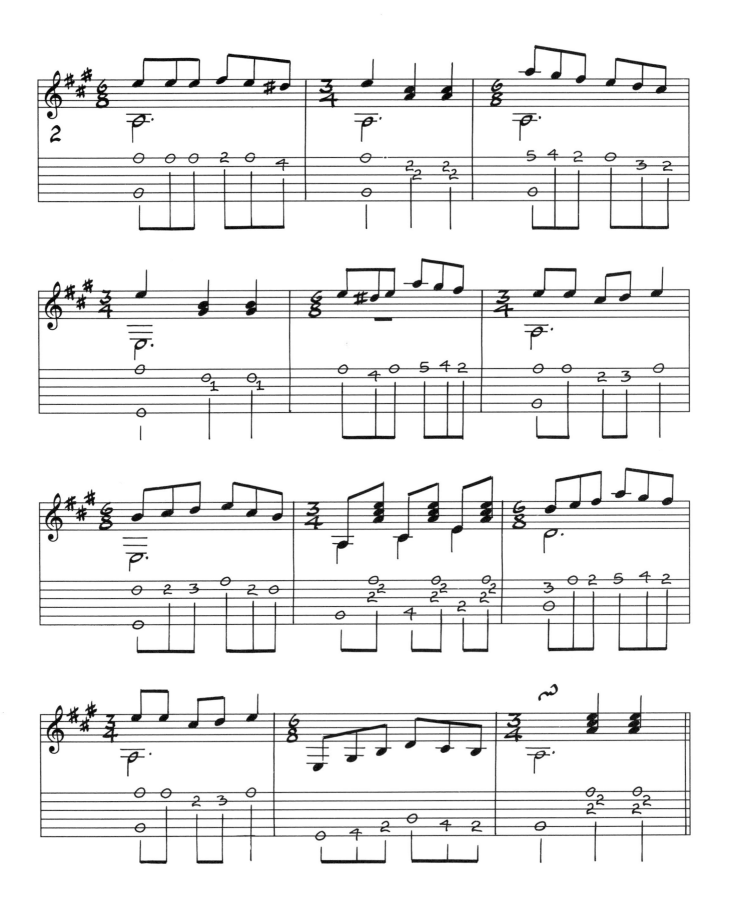

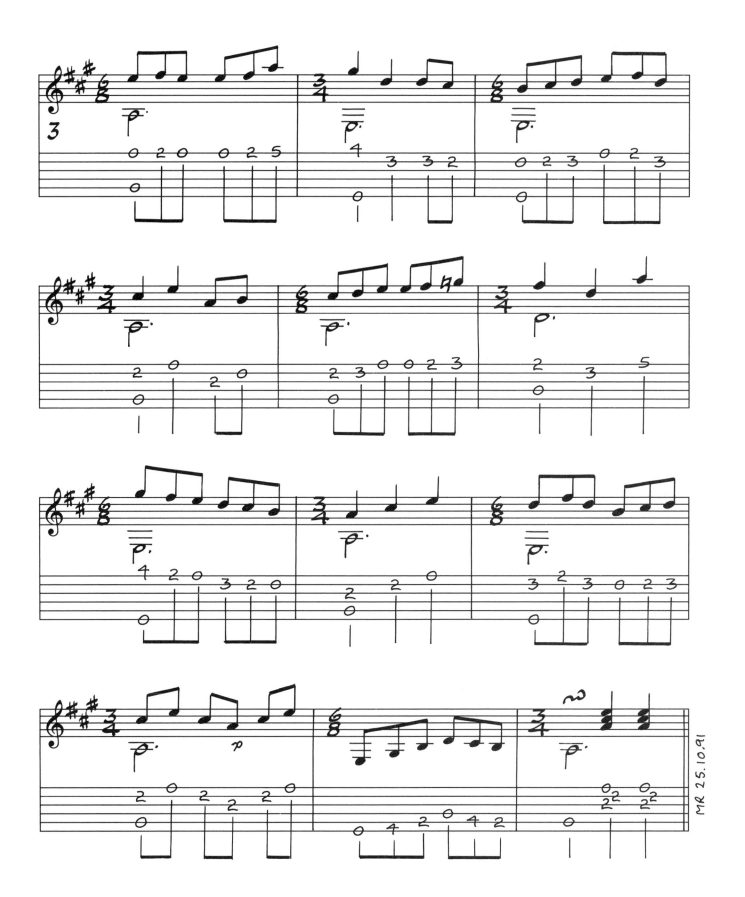

MR 25.10.91

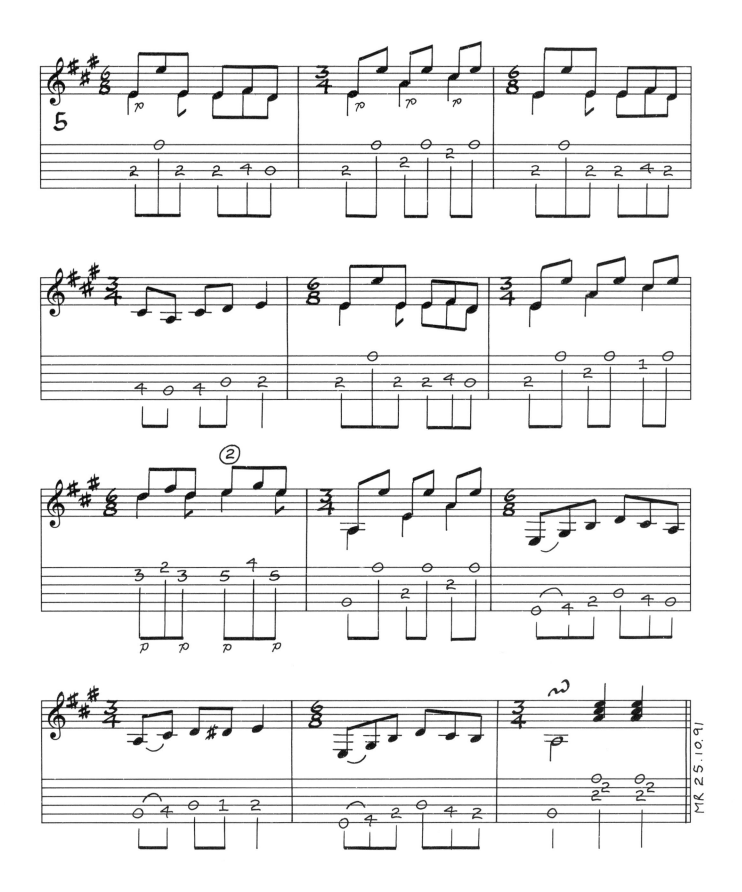

MR 25.10.91

10

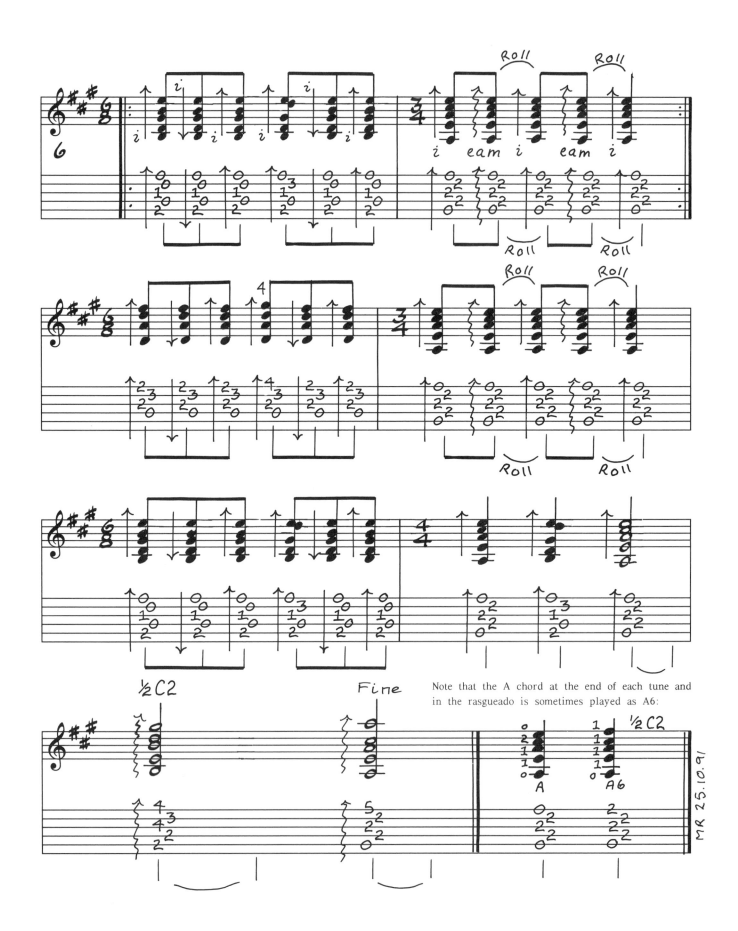

Note that the A chord at the end of each tune and in the rasgueado is sometimes played as A6:

MR 25.10.91

Mandrake

The mandrake is a medicinal herb with a forked root which has a resemblance to the
human body. This is a prelude in modern style by M.R.

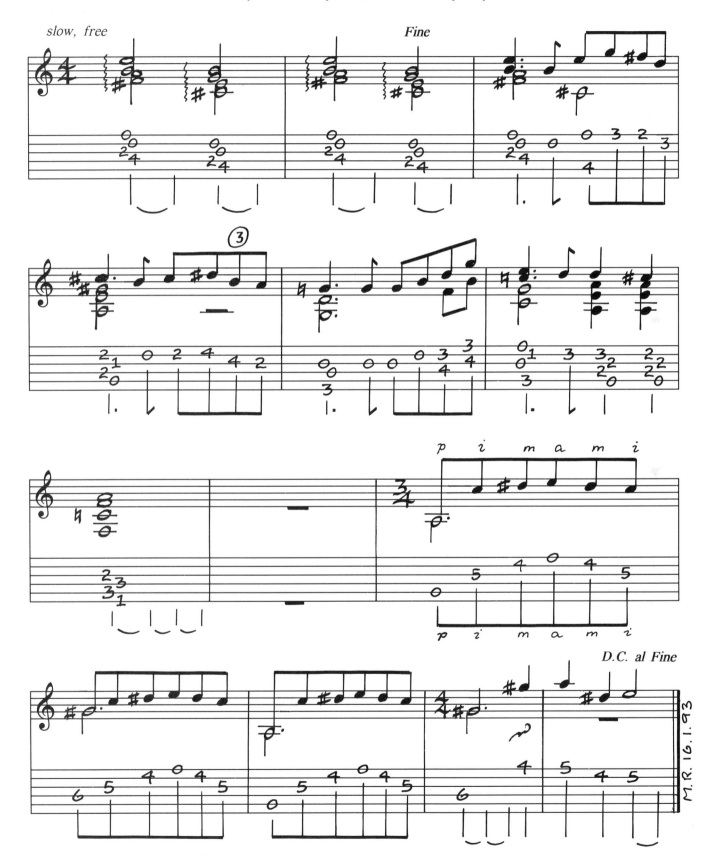

12

Cradle Song

Play gently, with a light touch. Original M.R. AA,BB,AB, end tag

End tag. (To end substitute this for the last bar, bar 16.)

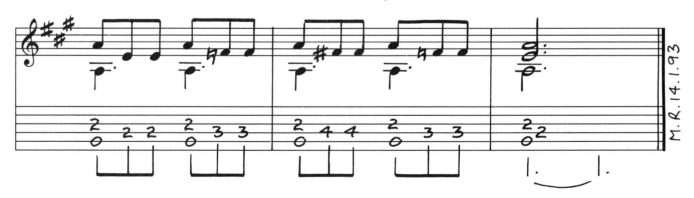

M.R.14.1.93

Cows in the Corn

This 'piper style' reel has four parts but all share the same chord sequence and,
indeed, many identicle phrases. Original M.R. As written x2.

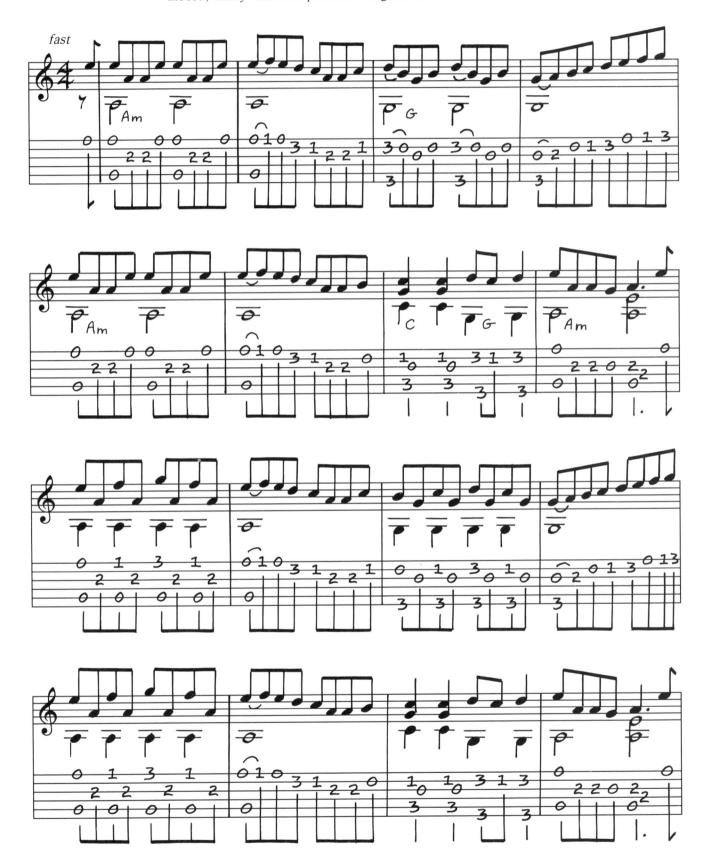

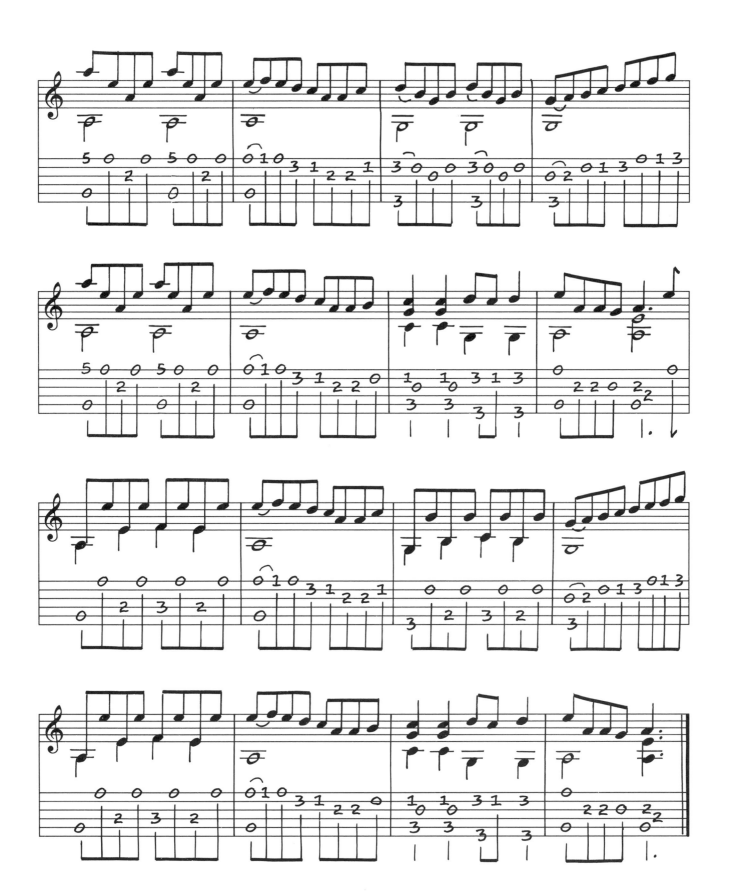

Mexican Serenade

A song tune by M.R. As written x2. Follow with Woodpecker Jig.

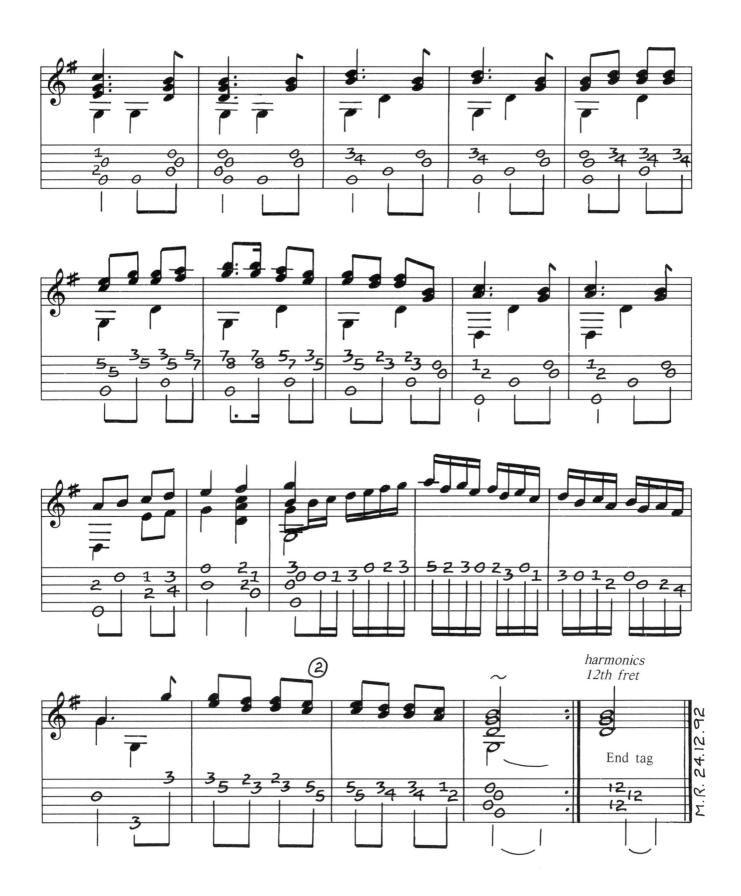

harmonics
12th fret

End tag

M.R. 24.12.92

Woodpecker Jig

Note the quadruplet figure in the B part. Quadruplets are quite common in jigs but are rarely notatated. Original M.R. (AA,B)x3. Precede with Mexican Serenade.

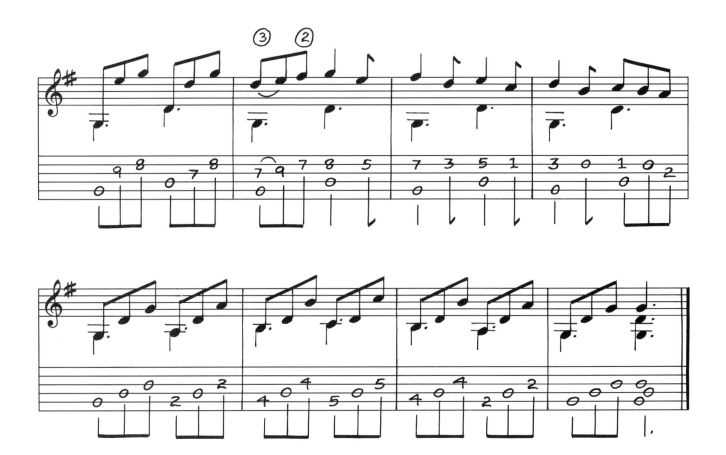

The author sometimes improvises a tremolo section and also uses a jig rasgueado.
The rasgueado is printed with Dargason in *The Star of Belle Isle*, page 47.

THE MAGPIE

Mills of Strata Marcella

Strata Marcella was a monastery at Pool Quay, near Welshpool. The mills were powered by
water taken from the River Severn. Original M.R. Play with expression. As written.

moderate, freely

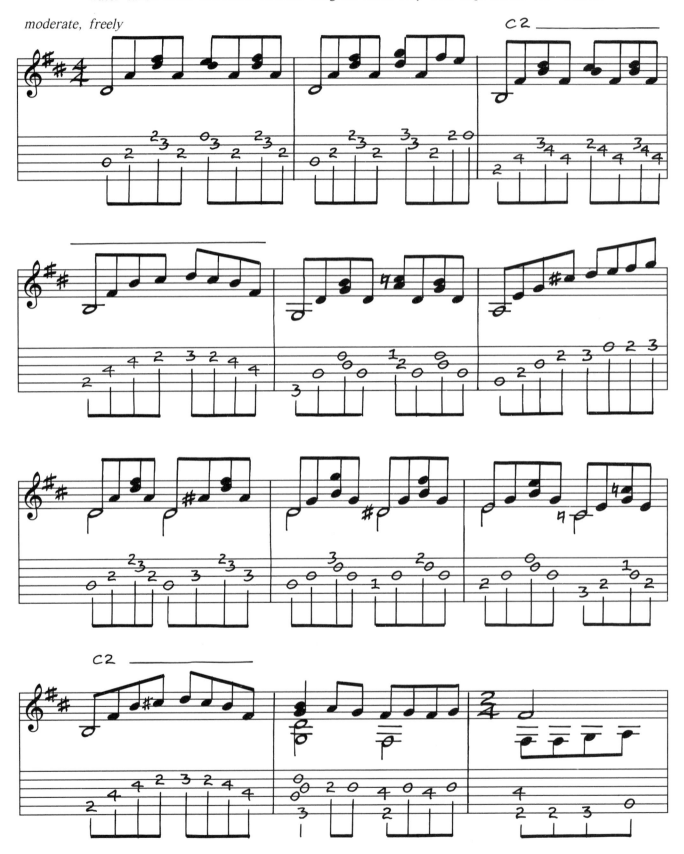

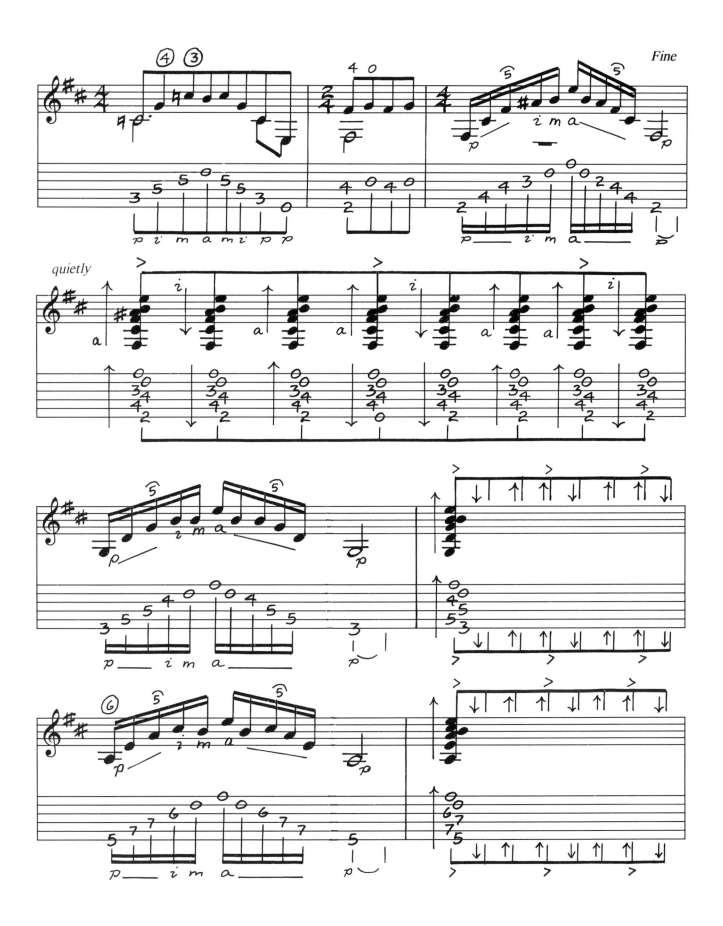

Fine

e = little finger

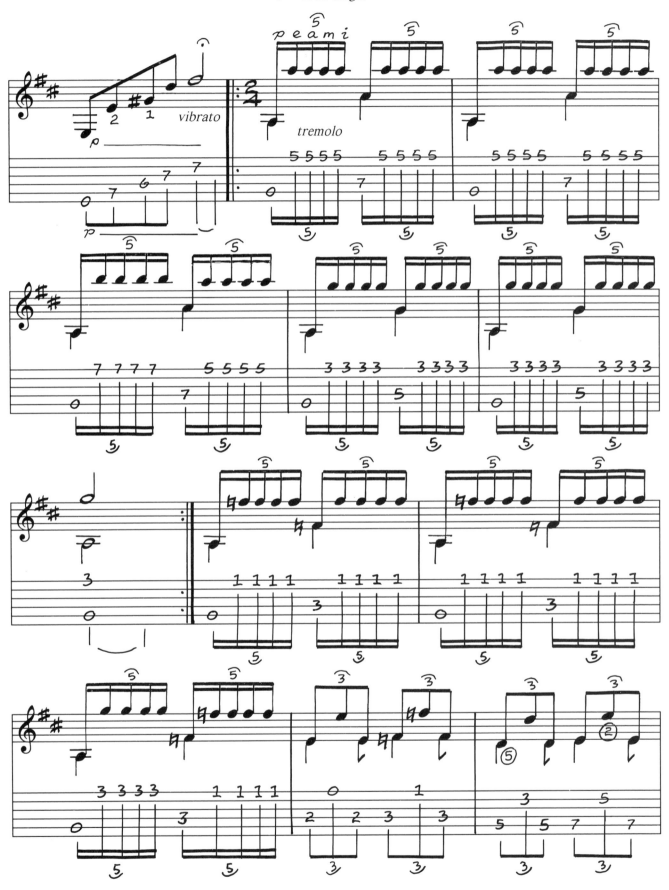

rest stroke

D.C. al Fine

7.8.92~4.1.93

Roaring Hornpipe

This tune has an unusual rhythm, a three bar unit that could be marked 18/8.
The ligados are important, especially the pulling-off from the off beat to the on beat.

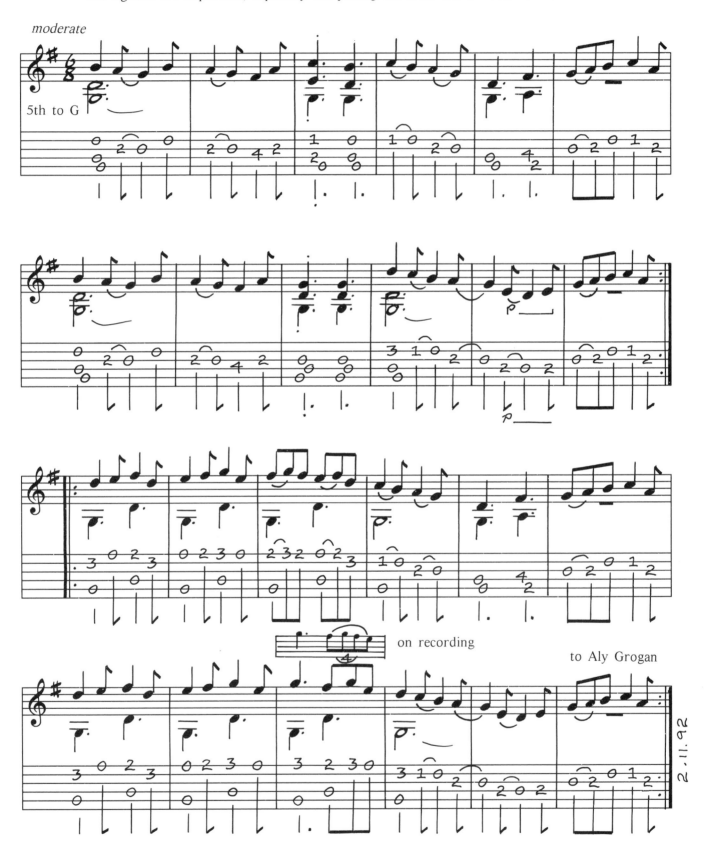

on recording

to Aly Grogan

Aly Grogan

The tune is from *Welsh National Music and Dance* by W.S.Gwynn Williams.
On the recording the Roaring Hornpipe and Aly Grogan are played as if they were one
tune, Aly Grogan being the C and D parts. Playing order: AA,BB,CC,D; ABCCD

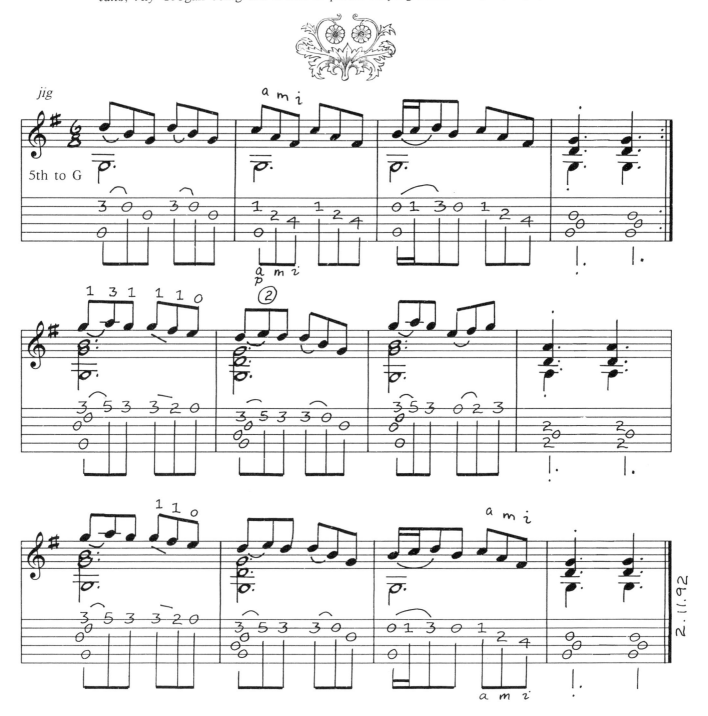

When pulling-off do not simply lift the left hand finger but pull it off, actually
plucking the string by pulling it sideways, towards the floor. A bit of string and fretboard
noise is not unwellcome in sturdy folk dance tunes like these. Indeed, without some they
can sound too refined. The author has done a lot of work using a guitar synthesizer
and what he missed most were the clicks, squeaks, rattles, buzzes and groans
that are so much a part of the acoustic sound. They have to be controlled but they do
have to be there.

My Last Farewell

An original tune by M.R. to the traditional words of My Last Farewell To Stirling (See *Raven's Nest* page 13.) On the recording the tune is played x2 as written, then in a simple variation as the first 6 bars as shown below, then as written again.

Cottage in the Wood

English traditional arranged M.R. As written x2. Play as the first in a medley
pair with Jockey in the Hayloft.

Jockey in the Hayloft

English traditional arranged M.R. As written x3. Play as second of medley pair
with Cottage in the Wood.

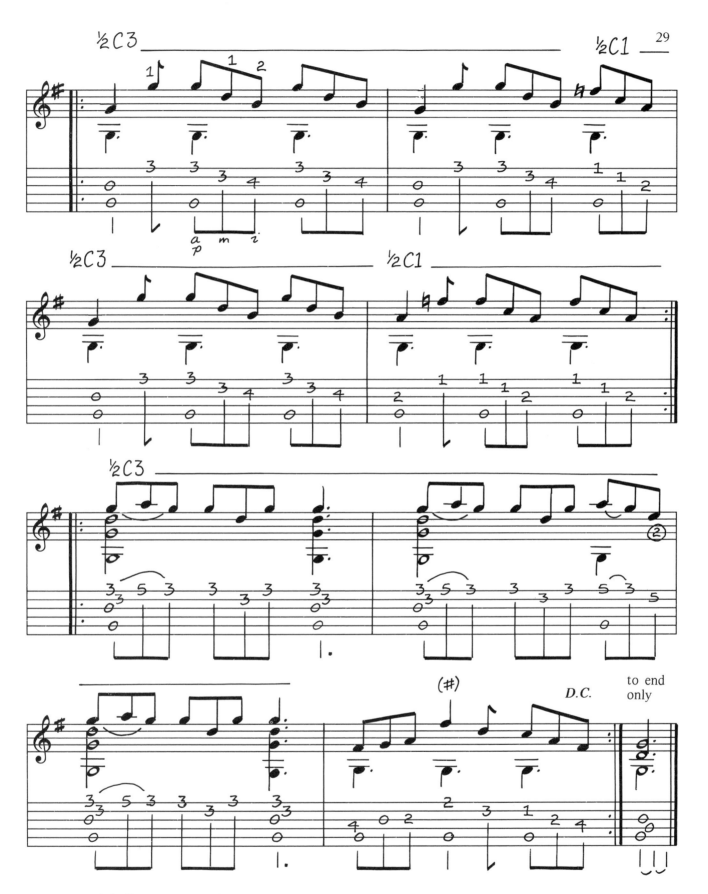

Triple jigs are very old and were popular in England long before they were exported to Ireland. They are often circular in structure, each section ending on the Dominant 7th chord, and can be strenuous to play because they rattle on relentlessly. Play with a lilt.

Bobbing Joe

Published by John Playford in his *English Dancing Master*, 1650.
The arrangement and reprise variations A1 and B1 are by Michael Raven.

Grimstock

Playford (1652) arranged with B part variation by M.R. As written x3.

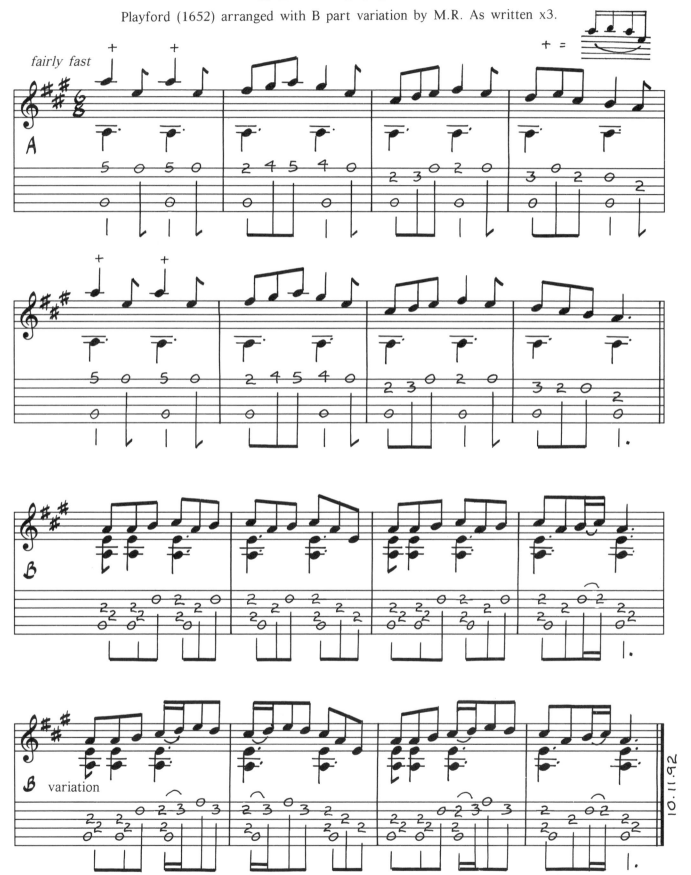

Milkmaid's Bob

Playford (1650) arranged with variation by M.R. As written x2.

Althea

Playford (1665) arranged M.R. Sounds modern and harmonized to match.
AA,AA,AB

Aniseed Water Robin

Playford (1650) arranged and adapted with reprise variations by M.R.
AA,BB,AB

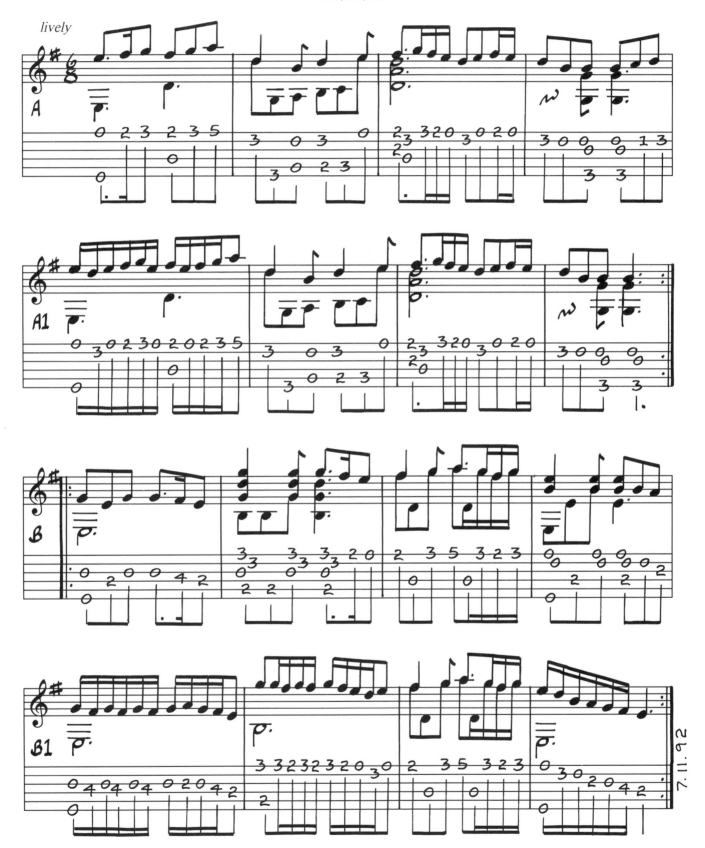

Mulberry Garden

Playford (1670) arranged M.R. As written x2.

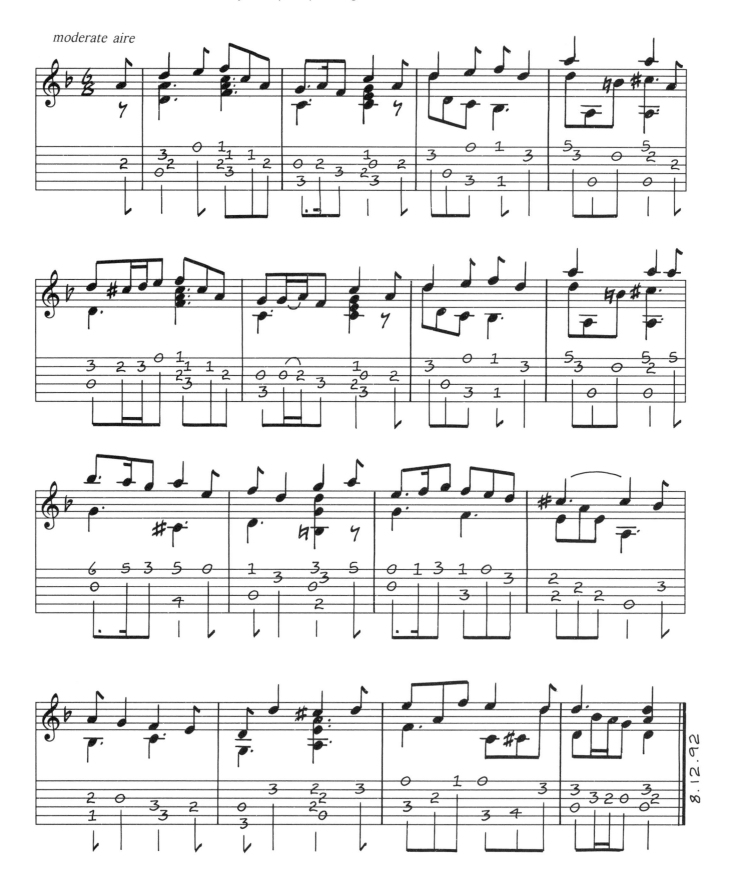

Saint Martin's

Playford (1650) arranged and adapted by M.R. AA,BB,AB

Perfect Cure

Long dance arranged with B reprise variation by M.R. Played as a slow aire.

AA,BB1,A

Lull Me Beyond Thee

Playford (1650) arranged and adapted with reprise variations by M.R.
AA,BB,AB

Jack a Lent

Playford (1650) also called Lord Caernarvon's Jig, arranged M.R. As written x3.

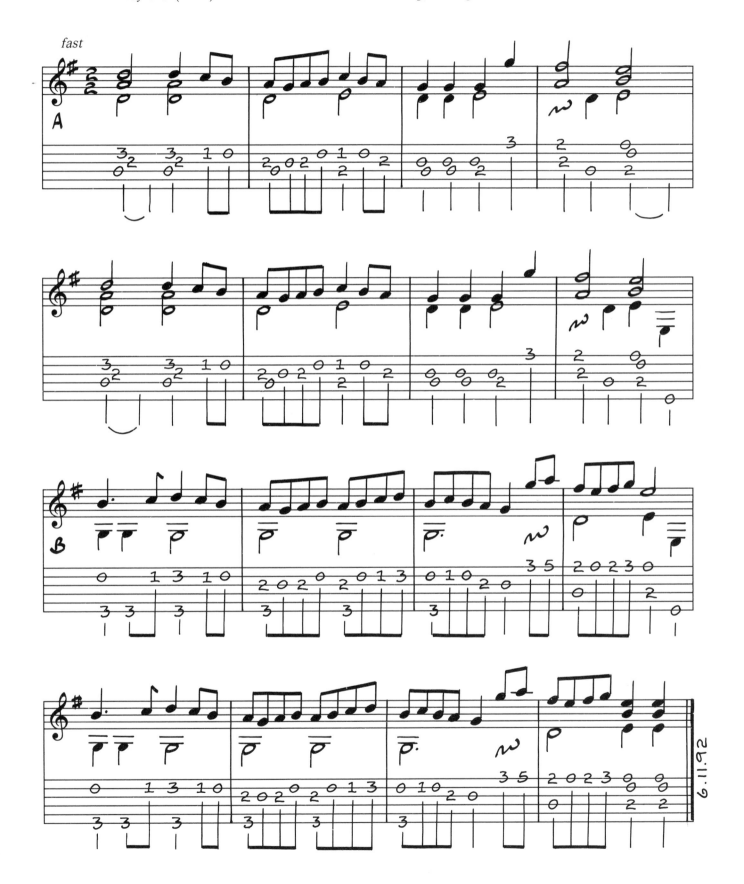

Never Love Thee More

Playford (1650) arranged M.R. As written x2.

slow aire

13. 11. 92

Bonny Grey-Eyed Morn

Popular in the 1690's. Dot the rhythm at will. For first line anchor the index
finger at the 3rd fret. As written x2.

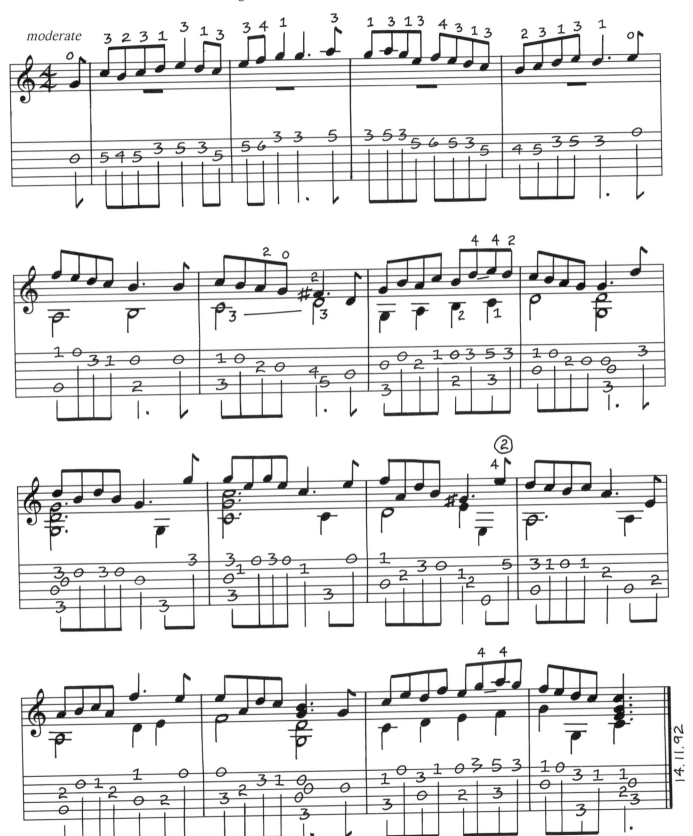

Painted Chamber

English c. 1680. Arranged here as an aire but can also be played as a jig.
ABBA

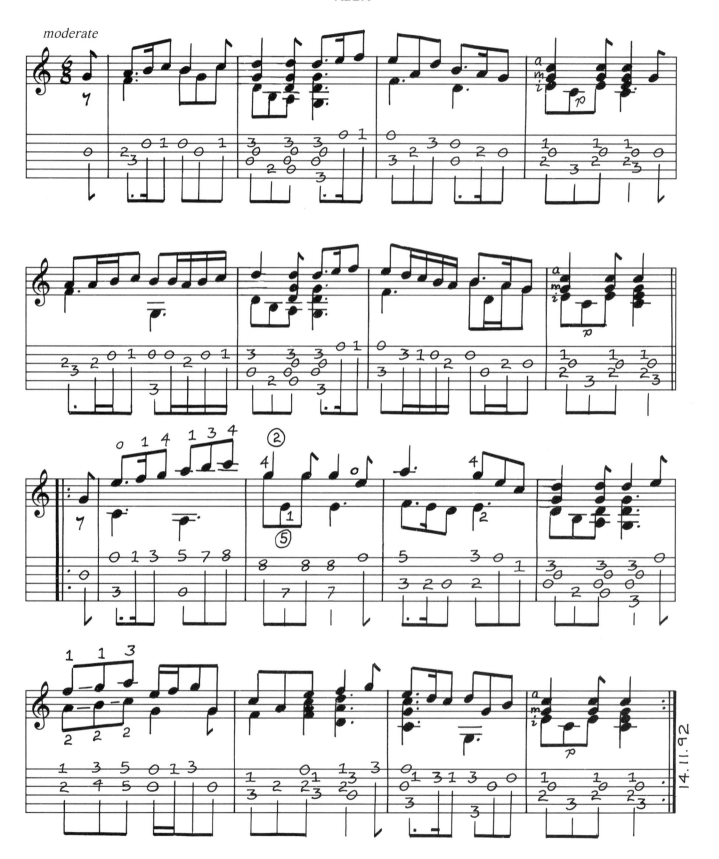

Rufty Tufty

From the *English Dancing Master*, 1650. Arranged M.R. (AA,BB,CC)x3

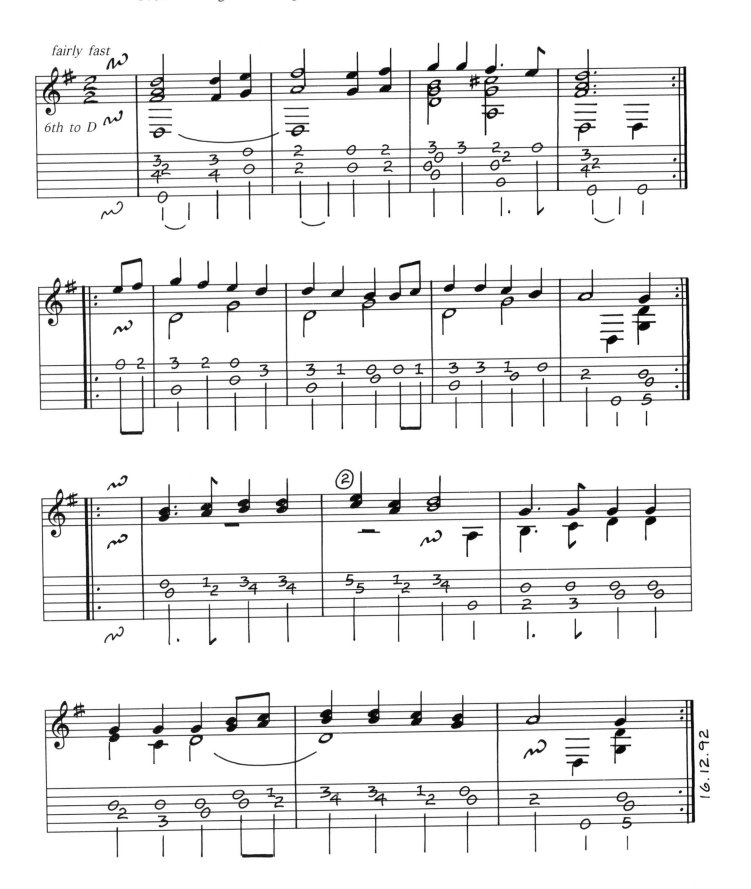

Red Velvet

A slow aire follwed by a moderate dance. Original M.R. A,BB,CC,ABC

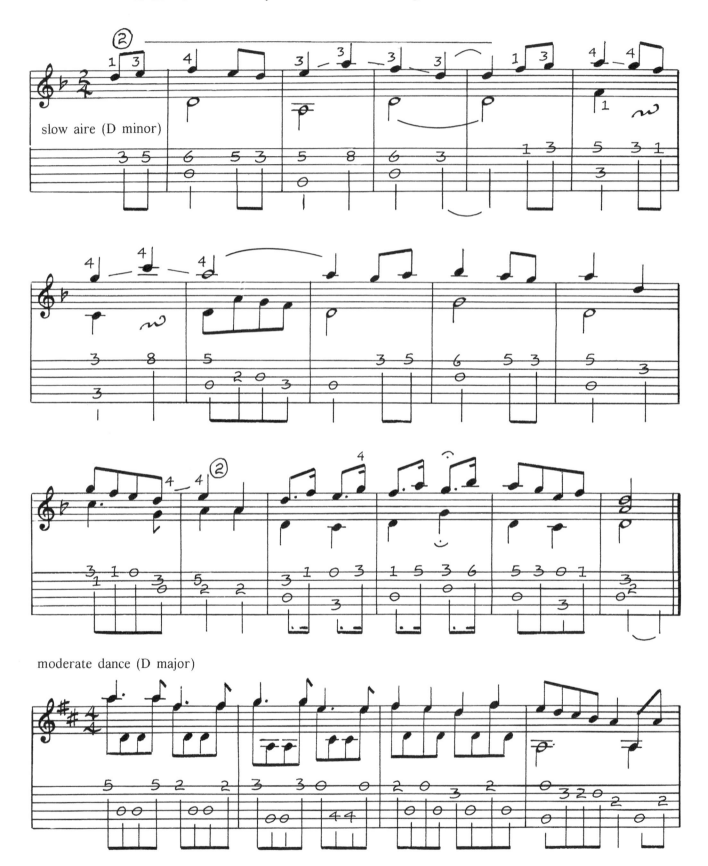

slow aire (D minor)

moderate dance (D major)

Silent Field

So sad to see a field once full of sheep now silent. Dorian mode.
Original M.R. As written. Follow with Swynnerton Blackbird as an aire – dance pair.

Swynnerton Blackbird

Note the syncopations chracteristic of the Old English Hornpipe in bars 3, 4, 7, 9, 15, and 16. Original M.R.

lively, Old English Hornpipe

Epitaph

For my mother, died 20th December, 1992. Original M.R. As written x2.

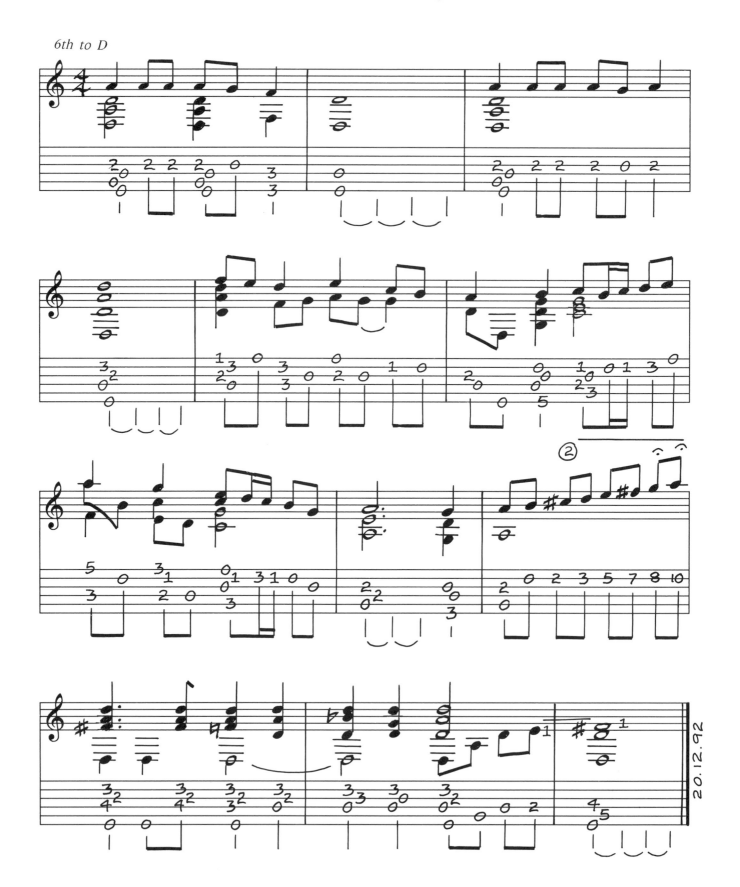

Marion Raven photographed in November 1939.
She is holding her son, Michael Raven,
then aged one year and 11 months.

Fair Land

This is the 1992 tune to the song. For the words and old tune see *Raven's Nest*.
This tune original M.R. As instrumental: as written x2.

damp

instrumental bridge

M.R. 23.12.92

Foaming Jug

Named after the pub near Kingswood Common, on the Shropshire/Staffordshire
border near Codsall. Original M.R. (AA,BB,CC)x2

moderate jig

Lady in the Dark

Playford (1665). Short, simple melodies, like this if repeated many times as a tune for dancing have an hypnotic effect, but not really suitable for solo performance.

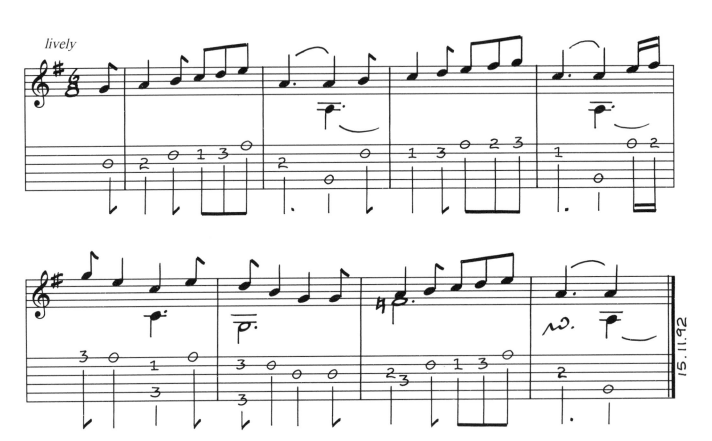

Lilting

Arranging folk dance tunes with only a simple bass drone is not only harmonically correct but also allows the performer can concentrate on lilting the tune. The most important elements of lilting are: 1) 'drops and raises', the playing of some notes so that they are barely heard whist accenting others so giving a pulse to the music; 2) slurring (hammering-on and pulling-off) especially from an off-beat to an on-beat, which gives a subtle syncopation; 3) ornamenting, especially with reverse mordents, turns, triplets and grace notes; 4) by playing lightly, this above all else. The classical musician is trained to make every note clean, pure and strong. This all too often results in a certain heaviness which is not suited to traditional music. 5) In slower tunes quaver pairs are often dotted. Lilted music sparkles.

Amora Strathspey

Strathspeys have a characteristically jerky rhythm. Note the 'Scotch Snaps'.
They are marked with an 'S'. Traditional arranged M.R. (AA,B)x2

Mazurca

From the playing of the Scottish group Ceolbeg. Arranged and adapted M.R.
(AA,BB,CC)x2

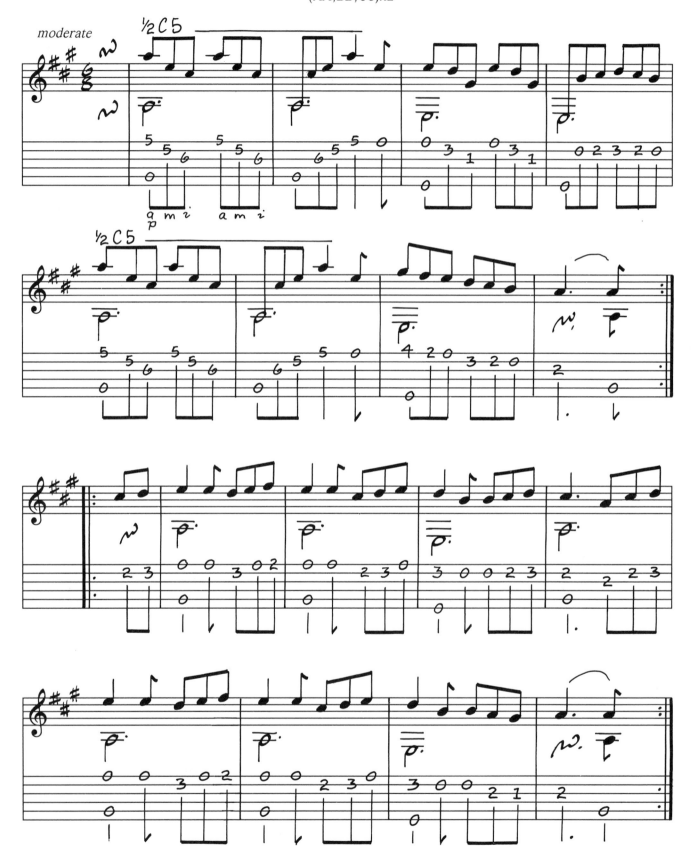

Schoon Lief

A fine Flemish Maying Song learned from the playing of the Belgian folk group, Rum.
For an English version see *Folk Songs of the Low Countries*, by M. Raven. Arr. M.R.

A Dew from Heaven

Belgian folksong melody arranged and adapted by M.R. As written x2.

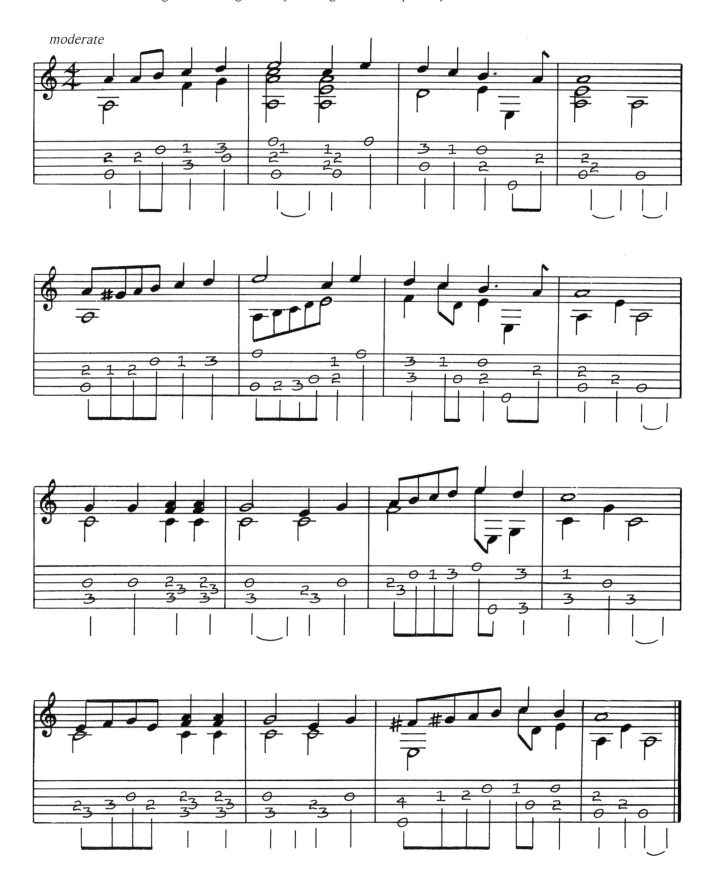

Autumn Leaves

They don't write them like this anymore. Adapted by M.R. from the splendid
arrangement by a gentleman from the South-West whose name is lost to us. As written x2

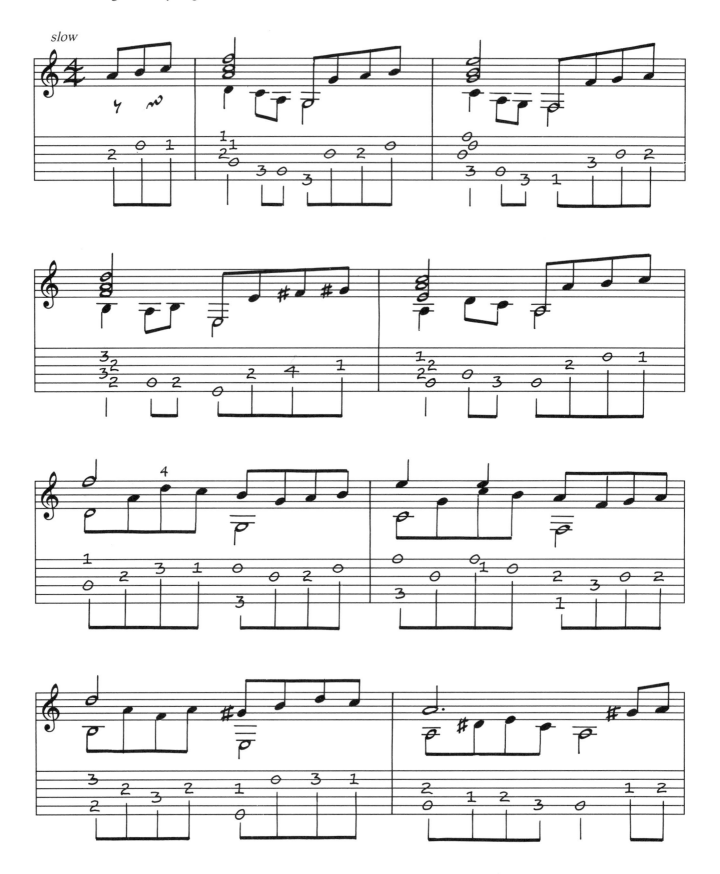

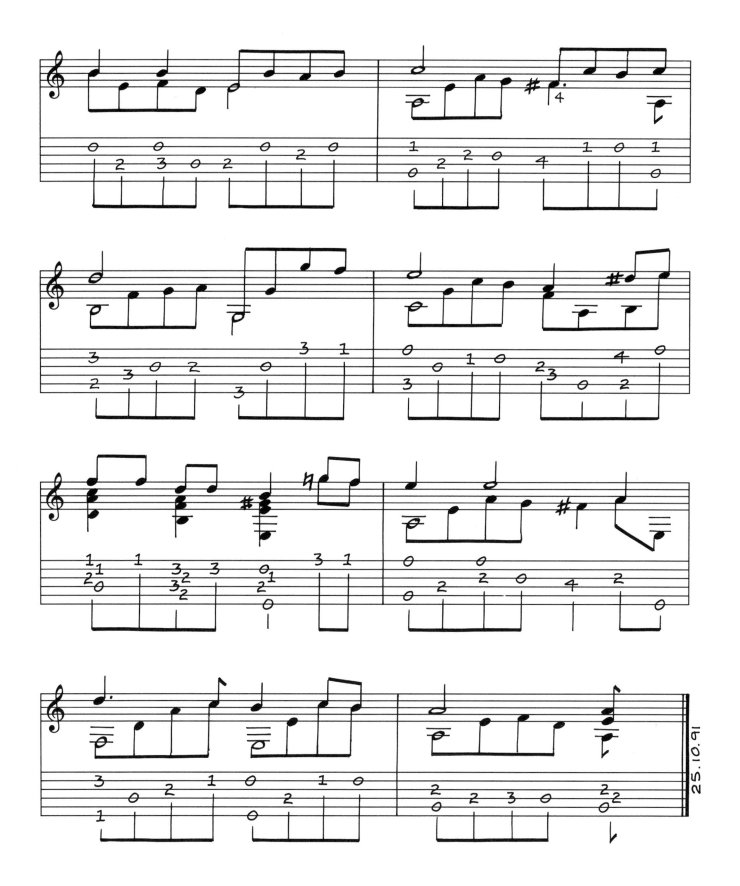

Printed by
Halstan & Co. Ltd., Amersham, Bucks., England

Michael Raven
1993 price list

26 Church Lane, Derrington, Stafford
ST18 9LY Telephone 0785 55555

Music for Guitar (5 book edition)	£14.95
Michael Raven: Guitar Music 1 & 2	£9.95
Michael Raven: Guitar Music 3 & 4	£9.95
The Complete Guitarist (tutor)	£7.95
Popular Songs for Guitar 1	£3.95
Popular Songs for Guitar 2	£3.95
English Folk Guitar 1	£5.95
English Folk Guitar 2	£5.95
English Folk Guitar 3	£5.95
An English Collection for Guitar 1	£2.50
Popular Tunes for Guitar 1	£3.95
Popular Tunes for Guitar 2	£3.95
A Variety of Guitar Music 1	£5.95
A Variety of Guitar Music 2	£4.50
A Variety of Guitar Music 3	£5.95
Chant of Falsity (guitar music)	£3.95
Popular Classics for Guitar	£5.95
Easy Duets for Guitar (Kuffner)	£3.95
Recuerdos de la Alhambra	£2.50
Guitarist's Good Book	£4.50
Popular Music for Guitar	£5.95
Popular Songs for Recorder 1	£1.75
Popular Songs for Recorder 2	£3.50
Popular Tunes for Recorder	£3.50
Tin Whistle Tutor	£3.50
1,000 English Country Dance Tunes	£12.95
Jolly Machine	£3.95
Raven's Nest	£3.95
Reynardine	£5.95
A Shropshire Lad	£2.50
Folksongs of the Low Countries	£3.95
Kempion	£3.95
John O'Barbary	£3.95
Hynde Horn	£5.95
Victoria's Inferno	£2.95
Urban and Industrial Songs	£16.00
Staffordshire and the Black Country	£9.95
Black Country Towns and Villages	£7.95
A Shropshire Gazetteer	£12.95
Shropshire Portraits	£5.95
Tarlton's Jests	£2.95
Midlands Digest, 6 books, each	£2.50
N E W G U I T A R B O O K S	(1993)
Soulton Hall, 36 aires & dances, etc	£5.95
Delbury Dervish, hymns, dances, etc.	£5.95
Wizard Beguildy, 35 country dances	£5.95
Lucy's Frolic, 35 country dances	£5.95
Silent Field, 36 aires and dances	£5,95
Star of Belle Isle 44 aires and dances	£5.95